River Rescue

Written by Peter Bently
Illustrated by Elisabetta Ferrero

WAYLAND

Tara and Dad were building a raft by the river at Starcross Stables.

Rocket, the sheepdog, was chasing butterflies.

Tara and Dad collected some big sticks, logs and rope. It took a long time to put everything together.

"I can't wait to try it!" said Tara.
"It's nearly ready," said Dad.

Plod the shire horse, Rascal the pony and Smokey the donkey, were in the field nearby, eating grass, but someone had left the gate open!

Plod, Rascal and Smokey ran out
into the woods.

Tara and Dad were too busy
to notice.

"There," said Dad. "It's finished."
"Let's see if it floats!" said Tara.

"All right," said Dad, tying a long rope to the raft. "But first we need to tie the raft to the bank."

Suddenly, Tara noticed that the animals weren't in the field.

"Hey," she cried. "Where are Plod, Rascal and Smokey?"

"Over there, in the woods!" called
Mum, running down the path
with a picnic.

Plod, Rascal and Smokey were having great fun, running through the trees and jumping over logs.

"Tara, you stay here with Rocket,"
said Mum. "Dad and I will
catch the animals."

Tara sat on the raft as Mum and Dad rushed off into the woods.

"It's a great raft, isn't it, Rocket?"
she said.

Then Tara had an idea.
"I'll just see if it floats," she said.

Tara pushed the raft into the river.
It floated very well.

"Come on, Rocket, let's lie on it
until Mum and Dad get back,"
she said.

Tara stepped onto the raft and lay on her back.

But Rocket barked and stayed on the bank.

"Woof! Woof!" Rocket barked more loudly.

"What's the matter, Rocket?" said Tara, sitting up.

Then she saw why Rocket was barking. She had forgotten to tie the rope, and the raft had floated away from the bank!

"Help!" cried Tara, as the raft drifted into the middle of the river. But no one heard.

"Woof! Woof! Woof!" barked Rocket.

In the woods, Mum and Dad heard Rocket barking.

Then, Rocket did a very brave thing.
He jumped into the water and
swam to the raft.

He grabbed the rope in his teeth
and swam back to the bank.

Rocket held tightly to the rope until Dad came running back.

"Good boy, Rocket!" said Dad, stepping into the water. He quickly took the rope and pulled the raft to the bank.

Tara began to cry.
"I'm sorry I went on the raft,"
she sobbed, as Dad helped her
onto the bank.

"Yes," said Dad. "You must never
play in water when you are on
your own."

"It's lucky Rocket was there," said Mum, arriving with Plod, Rascal and Smokey.

"Thanks for saving me, Rocket!" said Tara, hugging him tightly.

Tara was tired after her adventure and rode home on Rascal. Rocket chased after them.

"I think I'll stick to riding horses after all," said Tara. "Rascal is much safer than a raft!"

START READING is a series of highly enjoyable books for beginner readers. **The books have been carefully graded to match the Book Bands widely used in schools.** This enables readers to be sure they choose books that match their own reading ability.

Look out for the Band colour on the book in our Start Reading logo.

The Bands are:

Pink Band 1A & 1B

Red Band 2

Yellow Band 3

Blue Band 4

Green Band 5

Orange Band 6

Turquoise Band 7

Purple Band 8

Gold Band 9

START READING books can be read independently or shared with an adult. They promote the enjoyment of reading through satisfying stories supported by fun illustrations.

Peter Bently lives in Devon with his wife, Lucy and a ready-made audience of two children, Theo (9) and Tara (6). Apart from writing, he enjoys walking, going to the beach, meeting up with friends, and having family fun.

Elisabetta Ferrero works in Vercelli, a town in North Italy surrounded by paddy fields. She lives with her husband and two sons, a hunting dog who loves chasing rabbits but never catches them, six Burmese cats and a gold fish who is 11 years old!